TEST YOUR FINESSING

Finessing is one of the commonest techniques in the game and is one of the most important. How much do you really know about it? Do you invariably time your finesses correctly? Are you always confident of playing the right card, or even the right suit, for a finesse? Can you tell at a glance which finesses should be taken and which rejected?

If you have doubts in any of these areas, this book is for you. Author Hugh Kelsey, a grand master of bridge and a writer of world renown, invites you to test your skill in a finessing quiz which starts at a comfortable level but quickly becomes tougher.

The problems have been chosen to cover a wide range of situations where a finesse may or may not be required, and a study of them will bring both pleasure and profit. However well you score, you will arrive at the end of the book knowing more about finessing than you did when you began.

TEST YOUR FINESSING

by

HUGH KELSEY

LONDON
VICTOR GOLLANCZ LTD
in association with Peter Crawley
1981

ISBN 0 575 03004 6

Printed in Great Britain at
The Camelot Press Ltd, Southampton

TEST YOUR FINESSING

INTRODUCTION

The finesse tends to be neglected as a subject for serious study by bridge players. As one of the commonest moves in the game it is taken for granted. Everyone knows, or thinks he knows, all there is to learn about it. Yet there is more to finessing than meets the eye. On many hands the choice of card to lead for a finesse can make the difference between success and failure. When you have a two-way finessing position, there may be compelling reasons for finessing into one hand rather than the other. It may be a question of which suit to play rather than which card. Where there is a choice, a decision must be made about which finesses to take and which to reject. Finally, it may be a matter of abandoning all finesses in favour of a more promising line of play.

This little book is designed to test how much you really know about finessing. The problems are set back to back in order to reduce to a minimum the temptation to look at the answer before tackling each quiz. A bidding sequence is provided with each problem, but this is important only in so far as it helps to place the opponents' cards. The opening lead, and sometimes an account of the early play, is given, and at this point you should stop reading and try to work out the answer for yourself. If you have difficulty, read on down the page. In the section headed *Review* the problem is brought into focus, and in the summing up you may find some hints that will guide you to the correct approach. The solution and the full deal are given overleaf.

The problems are arranged in no particular order but they have been roughly graded according to difficulty, the easier ones coming in the earlier part of the book.

Beware of thinking that you have to look for a cunning finesse on every hand. These problems are concerned as much with avoiding finesses as with taking them.

You can consider yourself a good finesser if you get more than twenty of the thirty-six problems correct. More than twenty-five right makes you a first-class finesser and more than thirty an expert finesser. Good luck!

PROBLEM 1

♠ 9 6 5 3
♡ A 4
♢ 8 5 3 2
♣ 10 7 2

♠ 7
♡ K Q J 10 8 3
♢ A Q
♣ A Q 9 4

Love all.
Dealer South.

The Bidding

SOUTH	WEST	NORTH	EAST
2 ♡	Pass	2 NT	Pass
3 ♡	Pass	4 ♡	Pass
Pass	Pass		

The Lead

West cashes the king of spades and continues with a second spade to his partner's ace. How do you plan the play?

Review

There are eight tricks on top and chances of extra tricks in both minor suits. Ideally you would like to finesse twice in clubs and once in diamonds, but the entry position does not permit it. Dummy has one solitary entry in the ace of hearts, which means that only one finesse can be taken. Which one do you choose?

Solution

After ruffing the ace of spades and crossing to dummy on the second round of trumps, you should lead a diamond for a finesse of the queen. If the finesse succeeds you are home, since you can afford to lose two club tricks. If the diamond finesse fails, you still have some chances in clubs. Draw the outstanding trumps, cash the club ace and continue with the queen, hoping to pin a doubleton jack in one hand or the other (it would not help to find a doubleton king since there would still be two club losers).

The complete deal:

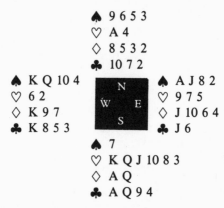

```
                    ♠ 9 6 5 3
                    ♡ A 4
                    ◇ 8 5 3 2
                    ♣ 10 7 2
    ♠ K Q 10 4                     ♠ A J 8 2
    ♡ 6 2           N               ♡ 9 7 5
    ◇ K 9 7      W     E            ◇ J 10 6 4
    ♣ K 8 5 3       S               ♣ J 6
                    ♠ 7
                    ♡ K Q J 10 8 3
                    ◇ A Q
                    ♣ A Q 9 4
```

It is true that on the lie of the cards you can also succeed by taking a club finesse. When the queen of clubs loses to the king, the same residual chance of finding the jack doubleton is available. What makes the club finesse an inferior play is that it does not guarantee the success of the contract when it succeeds, since East may have K J 8 x in clubs.

PROBLEM 2

```
                    ♠ Q J 5
                    ♡ A K
                    ◇ A J 7 2
                    ♣ A 10 9 3
                         N
                     W       E
                         S
                    ♠ A 6 3
                    ♡ 10 6 5
Game all.           ◇ 8 3
Dealer North.       ♣ Q J 7 6 4
```

The Bidding

WEST	NORTH	EAST	SOUTH
	1 ◇	Pass	1 NT
Pass	3 NT	Pass	Pass
Pass			

The Lead

West leads the ten of spades and dummy's jack is covered by the king. How do you plan the play?

Review

There are two tricks in each of the major suits and one in diamonds, so you need just four tricks from the clubs to make the contract. It looks as though you should succeed whether the club finesse is right or wrong. If you run a high club on the first round you can make sure of four tricks in the suit even if West has all the missing clubs. Can you see any snags?

Solution

The trouble is that it may be East rather than West who has all the outstanding clubs. Suppose the complete deal is as follows:

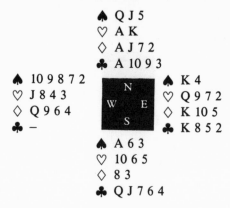

```
               ♠ Q J 5
               ♡ A K
               ◇ A J 7 2
               ♣ A 10 9 3
♠ 10 9 8 7 2                    ♠ K 4
♡ J 8 4 3          N           ♡ Q 9 7 2
◇ Q 9 6 4      W       E       ◇ K 10 5
♣ –                S           ♣ K 8 5 2
               ♠ A 6 3
               ♡ 10 6 5
               ◇ 8 3
               ♣ Q J 7 6 4
```

If you win the first trick with the ace of spades and run the queen of clubs, East will hold off. He will keep his king for the third or fourth round, denying you access to the fifth club in your hand and limiting you to three club tricks. With no real chance of an extra trick in any other suit, you will then have to go one down.

It is unnecessary to put the contract at risk in this way. To make certain of nine tricks you should reject any idea of taking the club finesse and retain the ace of spades as an entry to your hand.

Allow the king of spades to win the first trick. You can win any return in dummy and play the ace and another club, guaranteeing nine tricks no matter how the cards are distributed.

PROBLEM 3

♠ 7 2
♡ A Q 3
◇ J 4 3
♣ A K 8 6 5

♠ A Q
♡ 7 4
◇ A K Q 10 8 7 5
♣ 7 3

Love all.
Dealer North.

The Bidding

WEST	NORTH	EAST	SOUTH
	1 ♣	Pass	2 ◇
Pass	3 ◇	Pass	3 ♠
Pass	4 ♣	Pass	4 ◇
Pass	4 ♡	Pass	6 ◇
Pass	Pass	Pass	

The Lead

West leads the five of hearts against your slam. How do you plan the play?

Review

It appears to be an excellent slam, depending at worst on finding one out of two finesses right.

Many players lead aggressively against slams and it is quite possible that the heart finesse will work. If the queen of hearts loses to the king and a spade comes back, you could either take the second finesse or go up with the ace and try to do something with the clubs. The latter course looks superior, for you should be able to establish a long club if the suit breaks no worse than 4–2. Can you see anything better?

Solution

The trouble with finessing the queen of hearts at trick one is that if it loses East is likely to continue hearts in order to remove an entry from dummy. This will reduce your chances somewhat. After drawing a couple of rounds of trumps you can test the clubs, but with only one trump entry in dummy you will establish the clubs only when the suit breaks 3–3. The option of the spade finesse will still be open, of course, but your total chance of success will be no higher than 84%.

The complete deal:

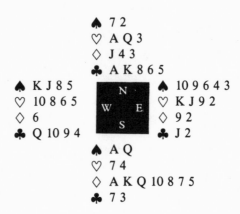

```
                    ♠ 7 2
                    ♡ A Q 3
                    ◇ J 4 3
                    ♣ A K 8 6 5
    ♠ K J 8 5          N          ♠ 10 9 6 4 3
    ♡ 10 8 6 5    W        E      ♡ K J 9 2
    ◇ 6                S          ◇ 9 2
    ♣ Q 10 9 4                    ♣ J 2
                    ♠ A Q
                    ♡ 7 4
                    ◇ A K Q 10 8 7 5
                    ♣ 7 3
```

The right move on this hand is to postpone the heart finesse. Play the three from dummy and allow East to win the trick. Since he cannot afford to return a heart into the tenace, East will probably switch to spades. You win with the ace, draw trumps with the ace and king and test the clubs, playing off the ace and king and ruffing the third round. With two entries remaining in dummy, you have no difficulty in establishing the fifth club for a discard of the queen of spades.

If the clubs had proved to be 5–1, you would have had to fall back upon the heart finesse or a squeeze. The total chance of success for this line of play is 92%.

PROBLEM 4

♠ K Q 4
♡ A J 5 3
◇ 9 4
♣ 8 7 4 2

♠ A J 9 5
♡ K 10 7 2
◇ 6 5
♣ A K 5

Game all.
Dealer South.

The Bidding

SOUTH	WEST	NORTH	EAST
1 ♡	Pass	3 ♡	Pass
4 ♡	Pass	Pass	Pass

The Lead

West leads the king of diamonds and continues with the queen, East following with the seven and the two. West then switches to the jack of clubs and you win with the ace. How do you plan the play?

Review

Two tricks have already been lost and a club loser seems unavoidable. The success of the contract therefore depends on bringing in the trumps without loss. In trumps you have a typical two-way finessing position. Do you propose to finesse through East or through West?

Solution

It looks like a fifty-fifty guess, and it is no more than that if the trumps happen to break in normal 3–2 fashion. The way you tackle the trumps could make a big difference if the division is 4–1, however. In that case you will be able to score four trump tricks only if someone has a singleton queen, or if *West* has a singleton eight or nine. The complete deal may be as follows:

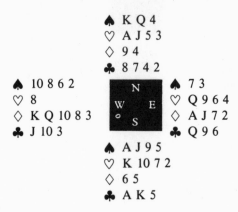

```
              ♠ K Q 4
              ♡ A J 5 3
              ◇ 9 4
              ♣ 8 7 4 2
♠ 10 8 6 2         N         ♠ 7 3
♡ 8                          ♡ Q 9 6 4
◇ K Q 10 8 3   W     E       ◇ A J 7 2
♣ J 10 3           S         ♣ Q 9 6
              ♠ A J 9 5
              ♡ K 10 7 2
              ◇ 6 5
              ♣ A K 5
```

To cater for this possibility you should start with the two of hearts to dummy's ace. Return the jack of hearts and run it if East does not cover. If East covers the jack with the queen and West shows out under your king, you can return to dummy with a spade in order to take a further finesse against the nine of hearts.

Note that there is no possibility of rolling up the suit if *East* has a singleton eight or nine.

PROBLEM 5

♠ 8 6 5
♡ J 10 7 3
◇ A Q 8 3
♣ Q 5

♠ A
♡ A K Q 9 6 5
◇ 7 6 2
♣ A K 4

N–S game.
Dealer South.

The Bidding

SOUTH	WEST	NORTH	EAST
2 ♡	Pass	3 ♡	Pass
4 ♣	Pass	4 ◇	Pass
6 ♡	Pass	Pass	Pass

The Lead

West leads the queen of spades to your ace. How do you plan the play?

Review

There are eleven top tricks and it looks as though you will have to rely on the diamond finesse for the twelfth trick. Can you see any way of augmenting your chances?

Solution

Certainly the diamond finesse represents the main hope, but it would be a mistake to take it on the first round of the suit. This is the sort of situation in which the finesse should be postponed. The chances of success can be increased significantly by playing on elimination lines.

After drawing trumps you should play a diamond to dummy's ace and ruff a spade in hand. Then cash three rounds of clubs discarding the last spade from dummy. The stage is now set for another diamond lead. If West plays low, you put up the queen. The complete deal may be as follows:

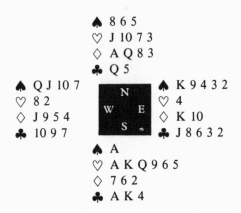

$\spadesuit$ 8 6 5
$\heartsuit$ J 10 7 3
$\diamondsuit$ A Q 8 3
$\clubsuit$ Q 5

$\spadesuit$ Q J 10 7 $\spadesuit$ K 9 4 3 2
$\heartsuit$ 8 2 $\heartsuit$ 4
$\diamondsuit$ J 9 5 4 $\diamondsuit$ K 10
$\clubsuit$ 10 9 7 $\clubsuit$ J 8 6 3 2

$\spadesuit$ A
$\heartsuit$ A K Q 9 6 5
$\diamondsuit$ 7 6 2
$\clubsuit$ A K 4

When East wins with the king he is end-played. The forced spade or club return allows you to discard the losing diamond from hand while ruffing in dummy.

This line of play makes sure of the contract not only when West has the king of diamonds but also when East has the king singleton or doubleton.

PROBLEM 6

♠ Q 5
♡ A K 10 7 2
♢ A Q J 3
♣ 8 5

♠ A 10 9 4 3
♡ 6 5
♢ 7 4
♣ A K Q 2

Game all.
Dealer North.

The Bidding

WEST	NORTH	EAST	SOUTH
	1 ♡	Pass	1 ♠
Pass	2 ♢	Pass	3 NT
Pass	Pass	Pass	

The Lead

West leads the two of diamonds. How do you plan the play?

Review

With seven top tricks you need two more for your contract. The additional tricks could both come from diamonds. West may well have led from the king, and it seems natural to take the diamond finesse at trick one. Even if the finesse loses, it is hard to see what East can do to harm your prospects. There can be no more than two diamonds to lose, and you should have time to develop a further trick in spades. Are you satisfied with this analysis or do you see hidden dangers?

Solution

It would be awkward if East produced the king of diamonds and switched to clubs, for this would attack the entries to your main source of tricks – the spade suit. The complete deal could be something like this:

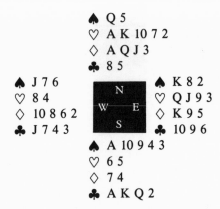

```
                    ♠ Q 5
                    ♡ A K 10 7 2
                    ◇ A Q J 3
                    ♣ 8 5
    ♠ J 7 6                         ♠ K 8 2
    ♡ 8 4                           ♡ Q J 9 3
    ◇ 10 8 6 2                      ◇ K 9 5
    ♣ J 7 4 3                       ♣ 10 9 6
                    ♠ A 10 9 4 3
                    ♡ 6 5
                    ◇ 7 4
                    ♣ A K Q 2
```

You could win the club switch and play a spade to the queen and king, but another club would come back and you would have to do some remarkably good guessing to make the contract.

The need for guesswork is avoided if you reject the diamond finesse at trick one. Play the ace of diamonds and run the queen of spades. That way you can be sure of making at least nine tricks.

PROBLEM 7

♠ J 4
♡ A 8 5
◇ A Q 10 5 4
♣ 6 3 2

♠ A K 5
♡ K 7 2
◇ 8 6 3
♣ A 10 7 4

Love all.
Dealer South.

The Bidding

SOUTH	WEST	NORTH	EAST
1 NT	Pass	2 NT	Pass
3 NT	Pass	Pass	Pass

The Lead

West leads the ten of spades. You try the jack from dummy but East covers with the queen, forcing out your ace. How do you plan the play?

Review

You need four tricks from the diamond suit if this contract is to be made, and there are various ways of tackling the problem. You might take a deep finesse of the ten of diamonds on the first round, or you could start with a finesse of the queen. Or is it right to reject any finesse and play the ace of diamonds on the first round?

[21]

Solution

If the diamonds are 3–2 with the honours divided you will always succeed by finessing twice in the suit. What about a 4–1 break? If West has any singleton you must always lose two tricks in the suit. If East has a small singleton, a finesse of the ten on the first round will succeed. So will a finesse of the queen, of course, for you can return to hand in hearts to play another diamond, ducking when West puts in an honour. If East has the singleton king, you will lose two tricks whether you finesse the queen or the ten. But if East's singleton is the jack, a finesse of the queen is the winning move.

The optimum play, therefore, is to finesse the queen of diamonds at trick two, catering for the following division of the cards:

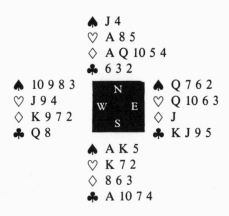

```
                    ♠ J 4
                    ♡ A 8 5
                    ◇ A Q 10 5 4
                    ♣ 6 3 2
  ♠ 10 9 8 3            N            ♠ Q 7 6 2
  ♡ J 9 4          W       E         ♡ Q 10 6 3
  ◇ K 9 7 2                          ◇ J
  ♣ Q 8                 S            ♣ K J 9 5
                    ♠ A K 5
                    ♡ K 7 2
                    ◇ 8 6 3
                    ♣ A 10 7 4
```

It is true that the play of the ace of diamonds on the first round succeeds when East has either the king or the jack singleton. But releasing the ace of diamonds causes problems in the more frequent cases where the suit breaks 3–2 with the honours divided. If West plays low on the second round you don't know whether to put in the queen or the ten. It becomes a guessing game, in fact, and you are likely to guess wrong half the time.

PROBLEM 8

♠ 6
♡ Q 10 4
◇ A K 10 7 6 5 2
♣ 7 3

♠ A 10 5 4 2
♡ A K 7 6 5
◇ 3
♣ A K

Game all.
Dealer South.

The Bidding

SOUTH	WEST	NORTH	EAST
1 ♠	Pass	2 ◇	Pass
3 ♡	Pass	4 ◇	Pass
4 ♡	Pass	5 ♡	Pass
6 ♡	Pass	Pass	Pass

The Lead

West leads the queen of clubs to your ace. Both defenders follow suit when you cash the ace of hearts. Needing to do something with the diamonds, you play a diamond to the ace at trick three and continue with a diamond ruff in hand. Both defenders follow suit, the jack appearing from East. How should you continue?

Review

Things have gone well so far. Now if you find the trumps 3–2 you might make thirteen tricks. But you need twelve tricks only. What is the safe way to continue?

Solution

You should continue with a low trump from hand. If West shows out there is nothing to be done. But if West plays a small heart you have a perfect safety-play in the finesse of the ten of hearts. If East wins and returns a diamond, you can ruff high, cross to dummy with the queen of trumps and enjoy the rest of the diamonds. The complete deal may be as follows:

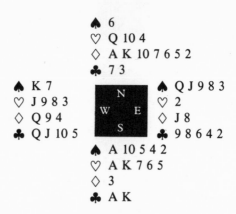

♠ 6
♥ Q 10 4
♦ A K 10 7 6 5 2
♣ 7 3

♠ K 7
♥ J 9 8 3
♦ Q 9 4
♣ Q J 10 5

♠ Q J 9 8 3
♥ 2
♦ J 8
♣ 9 8 6 4 2

♠ A 10 5 4 2
♥ A K 7 6 5
♦ 3
♣ A K

When you finesse the ten of hearts and East shows out, you simply abandon trumps and play diamonds from the top until West ruffs. You can win any return, cross back to dummy with the queen of hearts and score the rest of the diamonds.

If there is a bit of needle in the game, you can raise the temperature by asking West why he didn't find the killing spade lead.

PROBLEM 9

```
          ♠ 8 5 4
          ♡ Q J 4
          ◇ Q 10 6 2
          ♣ K 5 3

              N
          W       E
              S

          ♠ 10 3
          ♡ A K 6 2
          ◇ J 5
          ♣ A J 10 6 2
```

Game all.
Dealer South.

The Bidding

SOUTH	WEST	NORTH	EAST
1 ♣	1 ♠	2 ♣	2 ♠
3 ♣	Pass	Pass	Pass

The Lead

West leads the king of spades and continues with the six of spades to his partner's ace. East returns the four of clubs. How should you play?

Review

The defenders have already won two tricks and they are bound to win two more in diamonds, so you need to bring in the trumps without loss to make your contract. The club return gives you the chance of a "free" finesse against West. Should you take it?

Solution

When an opponent gives you the opportunity to make a play that you would not have attempted on your own, it is as well to suspect his motives. Without that trump return you would have tackled the trumps by leading low to dummy's king and finessing on the way back. Since East saw fit to offer you an alternative, it is likely that the normal play will succeed. You should therefore play low from hand on the first round of trumps.

The complete deal:

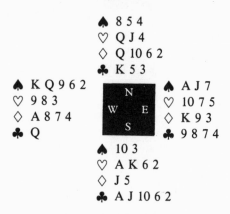

```
            ♠ 8 5 4
            ♡ Q J 4
            ◇ Q 10 6 2
            ♣ K 5 3
♠ K Q 9 6 2              ♠ A J 7
♡ 9 8 3        N        ♡ 10 7 5
◇ A 8 7 4   W     E     ◇ K 9 3
♣ Q            S        ♣ 9 8 7 4
            ♠ 10 3
            ♡ A K 6 2
            ◇ J 5
            ♣ A J 10 6 2
```

East judged that the defence needed a trump trick and realised that if his partner held an honour it must be a singleton. Hence his attempt to persuade you to waste an intermediate honour.

PROBLEM 10

```
              ♠ 6 4
              ♡ 7 6 2
              ◇ K 8 4
              ♣ A K 8 4 3

                    N
                W       E
                    S

              ♠ A K 7
              ♡ Q J 5
Game all.      ◇ A 7 2
Dealer South.  ♣ Q 10 6 5
```

The Bidding

SOUTH	WEST	NORTH	EAST
1 ♣	Pass	3 ♣	Pass
3 NT	Pass	Pass	Pass

The Lead

West leads the two of spades to the ten and king. How do you plan the play?

Review

Five club tricks will see you home, and you know that it is possible to bring in the clubs without loss even if the suit breaks 4–0 because you have a finessing position against either opponent. Which way do you play it?

Solution

The clue to the correct play is found in the opening lead. West appears to have led from a four-card suit, in which case it is a fair assumption that he does not have a five-card or longer suit. Players tend to lead from their longest suits against no trumps. It follows that West must have at least one club. Only East can be void in clubs, and you should therefore cater for this possibility by playing the queen of clubs at trick two.

The complete deal:

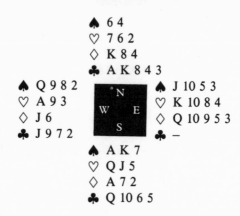

```
                    ♠ 6 4
                    ♡ 7 6 2
                    ◇ K 8 4
                    ♣ A K 8 4 3
        ♠ Q 9 8 2           ♠ J 10 5 3
        ♡ A 9 3             ♡ K 10 8 4
        ◇ J 6               ◇ Q 10 9 5 3
        ♣ J 9 7 2           ♣ —
                    ♠ A K 7
                    ♡ Q J 5
                    ◇ A 7 2
                    ♣ Q 10 6 5
```

When East shows out on the first round of clubs it is a simple matter to pick up five tricks in the suit by finessing twice against West.

PROBLEM 11

♠ J 9 4
♡ K J 6
◇ A 6 3
♣ A J 4 3

♠ A 8 3
♡ A Q 10 7 4
◇ 8 7 2
♣ Q 6

Game all.
Dealer South.

The Bidding

SOUTH	WEST	NORTH	EAST
1 ♡	Pass	2 ♣	Pass
2 ♡	Pass	4 ♡	Pass
Pass	Pass		

The Lead

West leads the five of spades. You play low from the table, East puts in the queen and you win with the ace. How do you plan the play?

Review

Although you appear to have four losers – a spade, two diamonds, and perhaps a club – it should be possible to reduce these to three. After drawing trumps you can try the club finesse, and even if this fails the club jack will provide a parking place for one of your losing diamonds.

Is there anything else to worry about?

Solution

Although it looks as though West has the ten of spades, you cannot be absolutely sure of this. It would cost East nothing to put in the queen from K Q 10 in an attempt to obscure the position. If you have to lose two spades you will need *three* tricks from clubs to compensate, and that will be possible only if East has the king along with not more than two small clubs.

The right play is to draw two rounds of trumps with the ace and jack, and then lead a low club from the table towards your queen.

The complete deal:

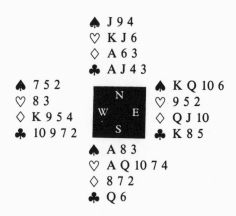

```
              ♠ J 9 4
              ♡ K J 6
              ◇ A 6 3
              ♣ A J 4 3
  ♠ 7 5 2                    ♠ K Q 10 6
  ♡ 8 3          N           ♡ 9 5 2
  ◇ K 9 5 4   W     E        ◇ Q J 10
  ♣ 10 9 7 2      S          ♣ K 8 5
              ♠ A 8 3
              ♡ A Q 10 7 4
              ◇ 8 7 2
              ♣ Q 6
```

If East plays the king he immediately gives you the three club tricks you need. If he plays low and allows your queen to win, you return to the ace of clubs, ruff out the king, and cross back to dummy with the king of hearts to enjoy a further club trick.

PROBLEM 12

♠ A 7 3
♡ 8 2
◇ K 10 8 4 3
♣ 9 6 3

♠ K Q 5
♡ A K J 10
◇ Q 9
♣ A J 5 2

Love all.
Dealer South.

The Bidding

SOUTH	WEST	NORTH	EAST
2 NT	Pass	3 NT	Pass
Pass	Pass		

The Lead

West leads the ten of spades to your king. How do you plan the play?

Review

There are six top tricks and you will be home if you can develop three tricks in diamonds. Two diamond tricks will suffice if you can score an extra trick in hearts as well. And one diamond trick will be enough if you can make four heart tricks. What is the best sequence of plays?

Solution

The establishment of the diamonds is complicated by the fact that there is only one outside entry in dummy. If you start with the queen of diamonds the defenders will no doubt allow it to win. You can finesse the nine on the second round, but if this loses to the jack the diamond suit will be dead and you will have to rely on finding East with Q x x in hearts.

The way to make sure of at least two diamond tricks is to run the nine on the first round. Now the defenders cannot profitably hold up. If the nine of diamonds wins, you continue with the queen of diamonds to knock out the ace and subsequently develop your ninth trick in hearts.

If the nine of diamonds loses to the jack, you can win the spade return in hand and overtake the queen of diamonds with dummy's king, again ensuring at least two diamond tricks.

The complete deal:

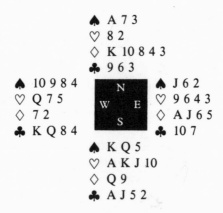

♠ A 7 3
♡ 8 2
◇ K 10 8 4 3
♣ 9 6 3

♠ 10 9 8 4   ♠ J 6 2
♡ Q 7 5   ♡ 9 6 4 3
◇ 7 2   ◇ A J 6 5
♣ K Q 8 4   ♣ 10 7

♠ K Q 5
♡ A K J 10
◇ Q 9
♣ A J 5 2

The first-round diamond finesse forces East to part with one of his stoppers immediately, after which you have no difficulty in establishing the suit.

PROBLEM 13

♠ K 7 4
♡ Q 10 9 3
◇ A Q 10 9 8
♣ 7

♠ A J 10 6 2
♡ A K J 6 5 4
◇ J
♣ 10

Game all.
Dealer South.

The Bidding

SOUTH	WEST	NORTH	EAST
1 ♡	Pass	3 NT*	Pass
4 ♣**	Pass	4 ♡***	Pass
4 NT	Pass	5 ◇	Pass
6 ♡	Pass	Pass	Pass

* Super-Swiss. Game values in support of hearts plus a singleton.
** Where's the singleton?
*** In clubs.

The Lead

West cashes the ace of clubs and switches to a trump. East following. How do you plan the play?

Review

There are nine top tricks and possibilities of developing extra tricks in either spades or diamonds. A direct diamond finesse will not help, but a ruffing finesse will see you home if East has the king. Alternatively you can play East for the queen of spades, cashing the king first and then finessing the ten. Is there anything else to try?

Solution

When there are finessing possibilities in more than one suit you should always try to combine the available chances in the optimum way. In this case the best odds are obtained by cashing the top cards in spades before trying the ruffing finesse in diamonds. After drawing the outstanding trump, play a spade to the king and a spade back to your ace. There is a 27% chance that the queen will fall. If the queen of spades does not appear, play the jack of diamonds to dummy's ace and run the queen of diamonds on the way back.

The complete deal:

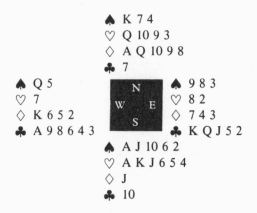

    ♠ K 7 4
    ♡ Q 10 9 3
    ♢ A Q 10 9 8
    ♣ 7

♠ Q 5   ♠ 9 8 3
♡ 7   ♡ 8 2
♢ K 6 5 2   ♢ 7 4 3
♣ A 9 8 6 4 3   ♣ K Q J 5 2

    ♠ A J 10 6 2
    ♡ A K J 6 5 4
    ♢ J
    ♣ 10

Your troubles are over when the queen falls on the second round of spades.

PROBLEM 14

♠ A J 2
♡ 10 6 3
◇ Q 5
♣ Q J 9 5 4

♠ Q 7 6 4
♡ 4
◇ A J
♣ A K 10 8 7 3

N–S game.
Dealer South.

The Bidding

SOUTH	WEST	NORTH	EAST
1 ♣	1 ♡	3 ♣	3 ♡
3 ♠	Pass	5 ♣	Pass
Pass	Pass		

The Lead

West starts with the king of hearts and continues with the queen of hearts for you to ruff. How do you plan the play?

Review

It seems a sound enough contract. There is a chance of finding West with a doubleton king of spades. Alternatively the diamond finesse may be right, although the diamond finesse may be unnecessary if the spades break 3–3. Do you foresee any particular problems?

Solution

The snag is that if you take a losing spade finesse East is sure to attack your options by returning a diamond. Expecting the missing kings to be divided between the opponents, you will no doubt go up with the ace and rely on a 3–3 spade break or a squeeze. But you may subsequently discover that West started with four spades and that East had both kings all the time.

To protect your diamond tenace, the spade finesse must be taken the other way. The right plan is to draw trumps, ending in dummy, ruff the third heart, play a spade to the ace, and return the two of spades towards your queen. If East plays the king "on air", your losing diamond is taken care of. If the queen of spades loses to the king, West may be end-played. At least you cannot be forced to make a decision in diamonds before you know whether the spades are breaking or not.

The complete deal:

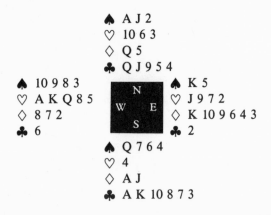

```
                    ♠ A J 2
                    ♡ 10 6 3
                    ◇ Q 5
                    ♣ Q J 9 5 4
    ♠ 10 9 8 3            N          ♠ K 5
    ♡ A K Q 8 5                      ♡ J 9 7 2
    ◇ 8 7 2       W         E        ◇ K 10 9 6 4 3
    ♣ 6                S             ♣ 2
                    ♠ Q 7 6 4
                    ♡ 4
                    ◇ A J
                    ♣ A K 10 8 7 3
```

PROBLEM 15

♠ 6 4
♡ A Q 10 3 2
♢ 8 7 4
♣ J 10 5

♠ K Q 5
♡ J 9 6
Love all.   ♢ A K
Dealer South.   ♣ A Q 9 6 3

The Bidding

SOUTH	WEST	NORTH	EAST
1 ♣	Pass	1 ♡	Pass
3 NT	Pass	Pass	Pass

The Lead

West leads the three of spades, East puts in the ten and you win with the king. How do you plan the play?

Review

Looking at the two hands, you note regretfully that four hearts would have been safer. Still, three no trumps has chances. A successful heart finesse would see you home, assuming a break no worse than 4–1. So, for that matter, would a successful finesse in clubs. But there are problems with entries. How should you proceed?

Solution

Anyone who sees an advantage in taking the heart finesse is the victim of an optical illusion. On this hand if the heart finesse is working there is no need to take it. The club finesse must be taken, of course, for it is important to keep East off lead and avoid a spade return through your queen. The right move at trick two is to play a heart to the ace and return the jack of clubs for a finesse against East. If the finesse loses, West will be unable to continue the spade attack without conceding your ninth trick, and after a diamond return you can still hope to find the king of hearts with West.

The complete deal:

```
                    ♠ 6 4
                    ♡ A Q 10 3 2
                    ◇ 8 7 4
                    ♣ J 10 5
     ♠ A J 9 3 2                    ♠ 10 8 7
     ♡ 8 7 5            N           ♡ K 4
     ◇ Q 10 6 5      W     E        ◇ J 9 3 2
     ♣ 4                S           ♣ K 8 7 2
                    ♠ K Q 5
                    ♡ J 9 6
                    ◇ A K
                    ♣ A Q 9 6 3
```

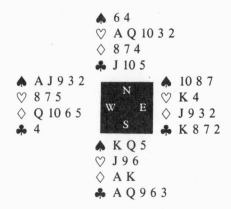

As it happens, the success of the club finesse solves all your problems. This line of play succeeds whenever the club finesse is right and also when West has both missing kings.

PROBLEM 16

♠ A Q 7 4
♡ A 10 5 3
◇ 6
♣ A Q J 10

♠ K 2
♡ 9 8 7 6 4 2
◇ K 10 5
♣ 7 3

Love all.
Dealer North.

The Bidding

WEST	NORTH	EAST	SOUTH
	1 ♣	Pass	1 ♡
Pass	4 ♡	Pass	Pass
Pass			

The Lead

West leads the king of hearts to dummy's ace, East discarding the three of spades. How do you plan the play?

Review

It's a blow to discover that you have two trump losers. Still, there are several distinct finessing plays that might bring in the tenth trick. A direct club finesse will produce a happy ending if West has the king. Alternatively you could take a ruffing finesse in clubs after discarding a club on the third round of spades. And the straightforward play of a diamond from dummy will yield ten tricks when East has the ace. Which method do you choose?

Solution

The answer is all (or none) of them. The contract is completely safe if you play on elimination lines. After winning the first trick with the ace of hearts you should play a spade to your king, return to the ace of spades, cash the ace of clubs, and then discard your losing club on the queen of spades. If this wins, ruff the fourth spade and exit with a trump. After taking his two heart tricks West, who can hardly have started with five spades in view of his partner's spade discard at trick one, will be forced to lead a diamond or a club, either of which gives you a tenth trick.

The complete deal:

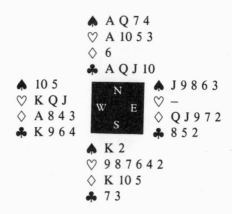

♠ A Q 7 4
♥ A 10 5 3
♦ 6
♣ A Q J 10

♠ 10 5
♥ K Q J
♦ A 8 4 3
♣ K 9 6 4

♠ J 9 8 6 3
♥ —
♦ Q J 9 7 2
♣ 8 5 2

♠ K 2
♥ 9 8 7 6 4 2
♦ K 10 5
♣ 7 3

It doesn't really matter if you take the discard on the third spade before cashing the ace of clubs. West may ruff, cash his second trump winner, and exit with a club, but now you have two trumps left in dummy to take care of your diamond losers.

PROBLEM 17

♠ 10 6 5 3
♡ –
♢ J 7 4 3
♣ A K J 7 2

♠ A 9
♡ K J 9 5 4
♢ A 10 9
♣ Q 9 3

Game all.
Dealer South.

The Bidding

SOUTH	WEST	NORTH	EAST
1 ♡	Pass	2 ♣	Pass
2 NT	Pass	3 NT	Pass
Pass	Pass		

The Lead

West leads the four of spades to the queen and ace. How do you plan the play?

Review

If the clubs run for five tricks you can count seven quick tricks. The hearts are too gappy to be of use, so you must hope to develop two extra tricks in diamonds with the aid of a double finesse. Do you foresee any difficulties, and are there any precautions you should take?

Solution

To finesse twice and then return to dummy to cash the thirteenth diamond you will need three entries to the table. That will be easy if the clubs are 3–2, but if clubs break 4–1 you may have to prepare a finesse in clubs as well as in diamonds.

To cater for a high singleton club – the ten or the eight – in the East hand, you should start unblocking by leading the nine of clubs to dummy's jack. A finesse of the nine of diamonds will presumably be won by West who, after cashing one high spade, will probably revert to clubs. You win in dummy with the king and drop the queen from hand when East shows out. Now you finesse the ten of diamonds and cash the ace. If the outstanding honour card falls, you return to dummy by taking the marked finesse of the seven of clubs. Five clubs, three diamonds and a spade give you a total of nine tricks.

Here is the distribution you are guarding against:

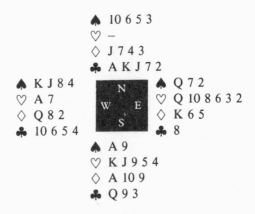

♠ 10 6 5 3
♡ –
◇ J 7 4 3
♣ A K J 7 2

♠ K J 8 4
♡ A 7
◇ Q 8 2
♣ 10 6 5 4

♠ Q 7 2
♡ Q 10 8 6 3 2
◇ K 6 5
♣ 8

♠ A 9
♡ K J 9 5 4
◇ A 10 9
♣ Q 9 3

If a high club does not appear from East on the first round, you must hope to find the suit divided 3–2.

PROBLEM 18

♠ 6 5 4 2
♡ A 5 2
◇ J 10
♣ Q J 7 3

♠ A K
♡ K J 10 9 8 4
N–S game.   ◇ A Q 7
Dealer West.   ♣ 6 4

The Bidding

WEST	NORTH	EAST	SOUTH
1 ♣	Pass	1 ♠	3 ♡
Pass	4 ♡	Pass	Pass
Pass			

The Lead

On the opening lead of the king of clubs East plays the eight. West shifts to the seven of spades which runs to your king. How do you plan the play?

Review

There are finessing positions in both hearts and diamonds, and you can afford to lose one trick in the red suits. It is tempting to play a second club at trick three in an attempt to set up discards for your losing diamonds. Is there any danger in this course?

Solution

It is far too risky to play about with the side suits before tackling trumps. Both black suits could be divided 6–1, in which case East would ruff the second club and give his partner a spade ruff, leaving you with an inescapable diamond loser.

The contract is a virtual certainty if you play with proper care. You should play the jack of hearts to dummy's ace and return the two of hearts. If East shows out on the second round, win with the king, play off the ace of spades, and exit in trumps. After taking his trump and his remaining high club, West will have to yield the rest of the tricks.

If East follows to the second trump, finesse the ten. If this wins you can draw the remaining trump and lead your club to make eleven tricks. And if West wins the second round of trumps? After cashing the ace of clubs he may be able to exit with a second spade, but you can cross to the table with the five of trumps and discard both diamond losers on the clubs.

In practice the complete deal turns out to be:

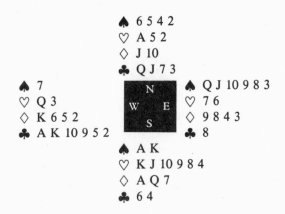

♠ 6 5 4 2
♡ A 5 2
◇ J 10
♣ Q J 7 3

♠ 7
♡ Q 3
◇ K 6 5 2
♣ A K 10 9 5 2

♠ Q J 10 9 8 3
♡ 7 6
◇ 9 8 4 3
♣ 8

♠ A K
♡ K J 10 9 8 4
◇ A Q 7
♣ 6 4

PROBLEM 19

♠ Q 10 6
♡ Q 7 4
◇ A 10 3
♣ A K 8 3

♠ A 5
♡ A J 5 2
◇ J 7 4
♣ Q J 6 2

Love all.
Dealer South.

The Bidding

SOUTH	WEST	NORTH	EAST
1 NT	Pass	3 NT	Pass
Pass	Pass		

The Lead

West leads the king of diamonds to dummy's ace. How do you plan the play?

Review

There are seven top tricks and at least one extra trick can be developed in hearts even if the finesse loses. It should also be possible to establish a second trick in diamonds. Are there any hidden dangers to watch out for?

Solution

There is some risk if you have to lose the lead twice before you can set up enough tricks for the contract. If you lead a heart for a finesse of the jack, West may produce the king and switch to spades. Now, if the spade honours are badly placed and the hearts fail to break 3–3, you will be in danger of defeat, for when West regains the lead with the queen of diamonds he will lead another spade to give his partner some tricks in the suit.

Since you can finesse either way in hearts, you should lead through West on the first round. You don't mind losing an early trick to East, who cannot profitably attack the spades. This is the sort of distribution you have to guard against:

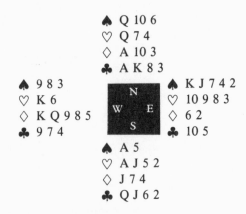

```
                    ♠ Q 10 6
                    ♡ Q 7 4
                    ◇ A 10 3
                    ♣ A K 8 3
   ♠ 9 8 3            N          ♠ K J 7 4 2
   ♡ K 6                         ♡ 10 9 8 3
   ◇ K Q 9 8 5   W       E       ◇ 6 2
   ♣ 9 7 4            S          ♣ 10 5
                    ♠ A 5
                    ♡ A J 5 2
                    ◇ J 7 4
                    ♣ Q J 6 2
```

Play a club to your queen at trick two and continue with a low heart from hand. If West goes up with the king you score three heart tricks and have no need of an extra diamond. If West plays low and dummy's queen wins, you switch promptly to diamonds to set up your ninth trick in that suit. Whatever happens, you are sure of four tricks in the red suits.

PROBLEM 20

♠ 10 9 3
♡ J 10 5
♢ K 10 8 4 2
♣ A Q

♠ A Q J 2
♡ A 6
♢ A Q J 6
♣ 10 4 2

Game all.
Dealer South.

The Bidding

SOUTH	WEST	NORTH	EAST
1 ♢	Pass	3 ♢	Pass
6 ♢	Pass	Pass	Pass

The Lead

West leads the five of clubs, putting you immediately to the test. How do you plan the play?

Review

With an unavoidable heart loser and finessing positions in both black suits, it is not a great slam. At a quick glance you might conclude that there is nothing for it but to try the finesses one after the other. Is there any case for doing otherwise?

Solution

Anyone who finesses in clubs is the victim of an optical illusion. The point is that the club finesse gains nothing even when it succeeds. With no way of avoiding a heart loser you would still be dependent on the spade finesse.

But if the spade finesse is right you do not need the club finesse, for the queen of clubs can be discarded on the fourth round of spades. The club finesse is quite irrelevant to the success of the contract. It is the finesse in spades that is the important one. You are home if East has the king of spades. Small prayers are more easily answered than big prayers, and you should go up with the ace of clubs at trick one, hoping to find the cards distributed something like this:

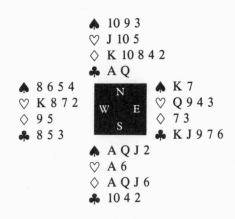

```
                    ♠ 10 9 3
                    ♡ J 10 5
                    ◇ K 10 8 4 2
                    ♣ A Q
      ♠ 8 6 5 4          N          ♠ K 7
      ♡ K 8 7 2     W         E     ♡ Q 9 4 3
      ◇ 9 5                          ◇ 7 3
      ♣ 8 5 3            S          ♣ K J 9 7 6
                    ♠ A Q J 2
                    ♡ A 6
                    ◇ A Q J 6
                    ♣ 10 4 2
```

After drawing trumps you run the ten of spades from dummy, finessing against the king. The queen of clubs goes away on the fourth spade and your only loser is a heart.

PROBLEM 21

♠ A 7 3
♡ A 9 4
♢ A K 6
♣ Q 7 6 2

♠ Q 9 8 6 4
♡ 5
♢ Q J 9 5 4
♣ 8 3

Game all.
Dealer West.

The Bidding

WEST	NORTH	EAST	SOUTH
1 NT*	Dble	3 ♡	3 ♠
Pass	4 ♠	Pass	Pass
Pass			

*15–17

The Lead

West leads the ace of clubs on which East plays the ten. West switches to the king of hearts. Dummy's ace wins and East drops the queen. How do you plan the play?

Review

Since East has been kind enough to indicate possession of Q J 10 in hearts, you know that West must have the rest of the high cards to make up the quota of points for his opening bid. East cannot have as much as a jack outside the heart suit. With the king and jack of spades sitting behind your queen, how are you going to avoid the loss of two trump tricks?

Solution

One way would be to cash the ace of spades and continue with a low spade from both hands, hoping to find West with K J doubleton. This is a slender chance, however. Both the bidding and the play of the hearts indicate that East began with seven cards in the suit and West with only two. If he has a doubleton heart he is unlikely to have a doubleton spade as well.

If West has three spades, your only hope is that East's doubleton includes the ten. In that case you can succeed by finessing against each opponent in turn. At trick three play the low spade from the table, inserting the six from your hand if East plays small. This preparatory move has been named the "intra-finesse" by Gabriel Chagas. You hope that your six will draw West's jack, the full hand being something like:

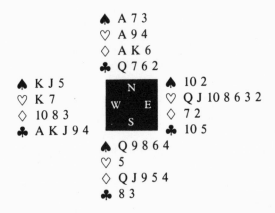

```
                    ♠ A 7 3
                    ♡ A 9 4
                    ◇ A K 6
                    ♣ Q 7 6 2
    ♠ K J 5            N           ♠ 10 2
    ♡ K 7         W       E        ♡ Q J 10 8 6 3 2
    ◇ 10 8 3                       ◇ 7 2
    ♣ A K J 9 4        S           ♣ 10 5
                    ♠ Q 9 8 6 4
                    ♡ 5
                    ◇ Q J 9 5 4
                    ♣ 8 3
```

When you regain the lead you play the queen of spades from hand, pinning East's ten and rolling up the trumps for the loss of one trick.

PROBLEM 22

♠ A Q J 4 2
♡ K 10 7 2
♢ 4
♣ A K Q

♠ 8 3
♡ Q 8 6 4
N–S game.   ♢ K 8 3
Dealer East.   ♣ J 6 5 4

The Bidding

WEST	NORTH	EAST	SOUTH
		1 NT*	Pass
2 ♢	Dble	Pass	2 ♡
Pass	4 ♡	Pass	Pass
Pass			

* 12–14

The Lead

West leads the queen of diamonds to his partner's ace and East returns the two of diamonds. How do you plan the play?

Review

You have available the same sort of inference as in the last problem. To make up the values for East's opening bid he must have all the missing high cards. That means you have a sure spade loser and you must somehow hold your trump losers to one trick, in spite of the fact that East has both ace and jack.

Solution

The right shot is to play low from hand at trick two and ruff in dummy. Then lead the ten of hearts with the intention of running it if East plays low. You have to hope that West has the nine of hearts. If East covers the ten with the jack, you win with the queen and return a heart, finessing dummy's seven unless the nine appears. This backward finesse represents your only chance. The contract cannot be made if East has A J 9 in hearts.

The complete deal:

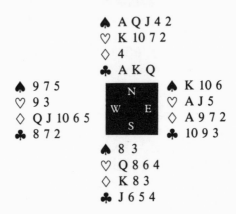

```
                    ♠ A Q J 4 2
                    ♡ K 10 7 2
                    ◇ 4
                    ♣ A K Q
      ♠ 9 7 5                        ♠ K 10 6
      ♡ 9 3            N             ♡ A J 5
      ◇ Q J 10 6 5   W   E           ◇ A 9 7 2
      ♣ 8 7 2           S            ♣ 10 9 3
                    ♠ 8 3
                    ♡ Q 8 6 4
                    ◇ K 8 3
                    ♣ J 6 5 4
```

Note that it is not the same to win the second diamond in hand and play a heart to the king and ace. On the second round of hearts you would then be reduced to guesswork. The ten from dummy is right in the actual case where East has A J x. But the ten would be fatal if East had A J doubleton.

PROBLEM 23

♠ 10 4
♡ 7 5 4
◇ A Q 8
♣ A K 8 5 3

♠ A K J 9
♡ A K
◇ K J 7 5
♣ J 10 2

Love all.
Dealer South.

The Bidding

SOUTH	WEST	NORTH	EAST
2 NT	Pass	6 NT	Pass
Pass	Pass		

The Lead

West leads the jack of hearts against your slam. How do you plan the play?

Review

This seems to be a fine contract. There are ten top tricks and you have the possibility of developing the extra tricks you need by finessing either in clubs or in spades. The clubs may provide two extra tricks even if the finesse loses. What are your chances of success and what is the right line of play?

Solution

The club suit can always be persuaded to yield four tricks except when West is void. In that case you will be short of an entry in dummy to establish and cash the long clubs. Nevertheless, careful play makes a certainty of the contract. Play a diamond to dummy's queen at trick two and return a low club to your ten. If the queen appears from either hand, your slam is guaranteed. You can be denied four tricks in clubs only when the complete deal is something like this:

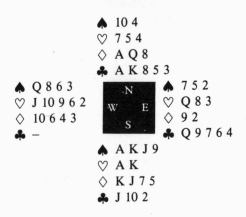

```
                  ♠ 10 4
                  ♡ 7 5 4
                  ◇ A Q 8
                  ♣ A K 8 5 3
  ♠ Q 8 6 3                      ♠ 7 5 2
  ♡ J 10 9 6 2    ┌───────┐      ♡ Q 8 3
  ◇ 10 6 4 3      │   N   │      ◇ 9 2
  ♣ —             │ W   E │      ♣ Q 9 7 6 4
                  │   S   │
                  └───────┘
                  ♠ A K J 9
                  ♡ A K
                  ◇ K J 7 5
                  ♣ J 10 2
```

If East plays low on the first round of clubs, your ten wins. Now there is no way of setting up the suit, but, with a cheap club trick in the bag, you can quite happily switch to spades. Cross back to the ace of diamonds and run the ten of spades. When the finesse loses you still have your twelve tricks.

PROBLEM 24

♠ 6
♡ A Q 7 3
♢ 6 4
♣ A J 8 7 4 2

♠ A K 4
♡ K 10 6
♢ A Q J 9 5 3 2
♣ —

Game all.
Dealer North.

The Bidding

WEST	NORTH	EAST	SOUTH
	1 ♣	Pass	2 ♢
Pass	2 ♡	Pass	3 ♢
Pass	4 ♢	Pass	6 ♢
Pass	Pass	Pass	

The Lead

West leads the queen of spades to your king. How do you plan the play?

Review

There should be no losers in the side suits, for the small spade can be disposed of either by ruffing it in dummy or by discarding it on the ace of clubs. The only real problem is to avoid the loss of two trump tricks. How do you tackle the trumps?

Solution

It may be possible to finesse twice in trumps against East, but it can never be necessary. If the trumps break 2–2 or 3–1 there is no need to finesse; you can draw trumps in straightforward fashion by playing the ace of diamonds followed by the queen. If the trumps are 4–0? Well, if West has all four trumps there is no way of avoiding two losers. If East has all the trumps, the position will be disclosed when West shows out on the play of the ace, and you can cross to the queen of hearts and return a trump for a deep finesse of the nine.

The complete deal:

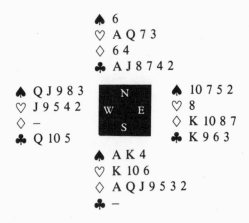

```
                    ♠ 6
                    ♡ A Q 7 3
                    ◇ 6 4
                    ♣ A J 8 7 4 2

    ♠ Q J 9 8 3                      ♠ 10 7 5 2
    ♡ J 9 5 4 2                      ♡ 8
    ◇ –                              ◇ K 10 8 7
    ♣ Q 10 5                         ♣ K 9 6 3

                    ♠ A K 4
                    ♡ K 10 6
                    ◇ A Q J 9 5 3 2
                    ♣ –
```

Note that an initial heart lead defeats the slam — barring a double-dummy finesse of the nine of diamonds on the first round. For the same reason you are likely to go down if you play a heart to the queen, or ruff a spade, at trick two.

PROBLEM 25

♠ Q 3
♡ K 7 5
◇ Q J 7 4 2
♣ A 7 6

♠ A J 6
♡ A Q J
◇ A 9 5 3
♣ K Q 10

N–S game.
Dealer South.

The Bidding

SOUTH	WEST	NORTH	EAST
2 NT	Pass	4 NT	Pass
6 NT	Pass	Pass	Pass

The Lead

West leads the nine of hearts against your slam. How do you plan the play?

Review

It's a pity about the duplication in hearts with 10 high-card points producing only three tricks. Still you have eight tricks on top and the diamond suit may provide the four extra tricks that you need. Apart from the diamond finesse are there any other possibilities?

Solution

Four tricks in diamonds can be guaranteed by adopting the safety play of starting with a low diamond from hand. This restricts the defenders to one trick in the suit even if someone is void. The trouble is that you don't know at this point if you can afford even one diamond loser. It all depends on what happens in the spade suit.

In order to find out how to play the diamonds you should first tackle the spades. Win the first trick in dummy with the king of hearts and play the queen of spades for a finesse against East.

The complete deal:

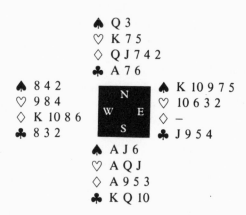

```
                    ♠ Q 3
                    ♡ K 7 5
                    ◇ Q J 7 4 2
                    ♣ A 7 6
  ♠ 8 4 2                          ♠ K 10 9 7 5
  ♡ 9 8 4            N             ♡ 10 6 3 2
  ◇ K 10 8 6     W     E           ◇ –
  ♣ 8 3 2            S             ♣ J 9 5 4
                    ♠ A J 6
                    ♡ A Q J
                    ◇ A 9 5 3
                    ♣ K Q 10
```

When the spade finesse succeeds, you know that you can afford to safety-play the diamonds. After winning the ace of spades, you play a low diamond to dummy's jack, return to the ace of diamonds, and continue with a third diamond to establish the suit.

If the spade finesse had lost to West, you would have known that you could not afford a diamond loser. After entering dummy with the ace of clubs you would have led the queen of diamonds, hoping to find East with K x or K 8 6.

[58]

PROBLEM 26

♠ A 9 5 3
♡ 6 4
◇ K 10 7 3
♣ A K 7

♠ K 8 2
♡ A K 10

Love all.   ◇ J 9 8 4
Dealer South.   ♣ Q 6 5

The Bidding

SOUTH	WEST	NORTH	EAST
1 NT	Pass	2 ♣	Pass
2 ◇	Pass	3 NT	Pass
Pass	Pass		

The Lead

West leads the five of hearts to the jack and king. How do you plan the play?

Review

There are seven top winners and you need to develop two extra tricks. The obvious place to look for them is in the diamond suit, and it looks as though you will have to rely on finding West with the queen of diamonds. Is there anything better than the diamond finesse?

[59]

Solution

There is no need to take the diamond finesse – at least not on the first round. You can afford to lose two diamond tricks as long as you lose the first one to West, who cannot press home the attack in hearts because of your tenace holding. What you must avoid is taking a losing diamond finesse into the East hand, for then a heart return could be fatal.

The right play is to cross to dummy in clubs at trick two and return a low diamond from the table.

The complete deal:

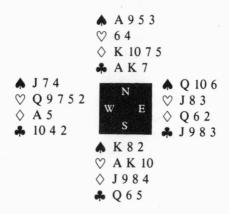

```
               ♠ A 9 5 3
               ♡ 6 4
               ◇ K 10 7 5
               ♣ A K 7
  ♠ J 7 4                      ♠ Q 10 6
  ♡ Q 9 7 5 2        N         ♡ J 8 3
  ◇ A 5          W       E     ◇ Q 6 2
  ♣ 10 4 2           S         ♣ J 9 8 3
               ♠ K 8 2
               ♡ A K 10
               ◇ J 9 8 4
               ♣ Q 6 5
```

East would need to be gifted with second sight to rise with the queen of diamonds on the first round. It is a virtual certainty that he will play low, hoping to be allowed to score his queen later. And once East plays low your contract is safe.

[60]

PROBLEM 27

♠ A 9 4 3
♡ 8 5 3
◇ K 9 6 4
♣ K 5

♠ K 10 7 6 2
♡ A 4
◇ A Q 8
♣ A J 7

N–S game.
Dealer South.

The Bidding

SOUTH	WEST	NORTH	EAST
1 ♠	2 ♠*	3 ♠	Pass
4 ♣	Pass	4 ◇	Pass
6 ♠	Pass	Pass	Pass

* Michaels cue-bid, showing hearts and a minor.

The Lead

West leads the king of hearts, which you win. When you play a low spade to dummy's ace West shows out, discarding a heart. How should you continue?

Review

You can restrict East to one trump trick easily enough, but what is to be done about your heart loser? West can hardly have seven hearts, so you must dispose of the loser before giving East his trump trick. It is no good hoping for a 3–3 diamond split, because East would be able to ruff the thirteenth diamond and still score a trump trick. What else is there to try?

Solution

You will be able to discard your losing heart only if you can make four diamond tricks and if East has to follow to four rounds of the suit. One possibility is to play for West to have J 10 doubleton, but there is a far better chance that he will have a small doubleton.

The right play, therefore, is to take a deep finesse against East on the first round of diamonds. After the ace of spades, play a small diamond and insert the eight if East plays low, hoping for the full deal to be:

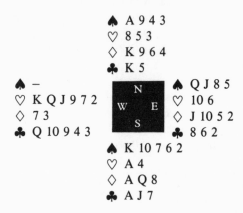

```
                    ♠ A 9 4 3
                    ♡ 8 5 3
                    ◇ K 9 6 4
                    ♣ K 5
    ♠ -                            ♠ Q J 8 5
    ♡ K Q J 9 7 2      N           ♡ 10 6
    ◇ 7 3          W       E       ◇ J 10 5 2
    ♣ Q 10 9 4 3       S           ♣ 8 6 2
                    ♠ K 10 7 6 2
                    ♡ A 4
                    ◇ A Q 8
                    ♣ A J 7
```

If East splits his honours on the first round of diamonds, you win with the queen, cross to the king of clubs, and play another diamond for a finesse of the eight. After cashing the aces of diamonds and clubs, you ruff the jack of clubs on the table, discard the losing heart on the king of diamonds, and finally play the small trump from the table, forcing East to split his honours once again and ensuring the loss of just one trick in trumps.

PROBLEM 28

♠ K 10 9 5 4
♥ A Q 3
♦ J 6 3
♣ 6 4

♠ A Q 7 3
♥ K 6
♦ Q 8 5 4
♣ A Q 7

Game all.
Dealer South.

The Bidding

SOUTH	WEST	NORTH	EAST
1 NT	Pass	2 ♥	Pass
2 ♠	Pass	3 NT	Pass
4 ♠	Pass	Pass	Pass

The Lead

You become declarer in four spades after a transfer sequence. West leads the ten of hearts, and when dummy goes down you wish you had passed three no trumps, a contract with nine top tricks. How do you plan to make four spades?

Review

There must be good chances of making ten tricks in spades. You are always home if the club finesse works, for a start. Alternatively you might find someone with a doubleton ace or king in diamonds. If you can set up a diamond winner without allowing East to gain the lead you may be able to avoid the club finesse. Is there anything better?

Solution

As a matter of fact, if the trumps break reasonably, there is no need to bother with finesses at all on this hand. The sure way of making the contract is to play on elimination lines. After drawing trumps you play two more rounds of hearts, discarding the small club from your hand. Then play the ace of clubs followed by the queen. Whoever wins the trick will have to choose between opening up the diamonds or conceding a ruff and discard, either of which gives you the tenth trick.

The complete deal:

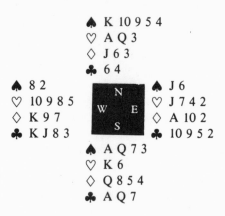

```
                ♠ K 10 9 5 4
                ♡ A Q 3
                ◇ J 6 3
                ♣ 6 4
♠ 8 2                           ♠ J 6
♡ 10 9 8 5          N           ♡ J 7 4 2
◇ K 9 7        W        E       ◇ A 10 2
♣ K J 8 3           S           ♣ 10 9 5 2
                ♠ A Q 7 3
                ♡ K 6
                ◇ Q 8 5 4
                ♣ A Q 7
```

Even in a pairs game you should resist the temptation to take the club finesse, for it is unlikely to produce an extra trick even if it works. Left to tackle the diamonds yourself, you must expect to lose three tricks in the suit. At pairs you should hope for the club king to be with West, in which case anyone playing in three no trumps may be held to nine tricks.

PROBLEM 29

♠ A 10 3
♡ J 9 4
◇ 8 6 5 2
♣ 7 6 3

♠ K J 5
♡ A 10 8 2
◇ A K 4
♣ K Q J

Love all.
Dealer South.

The Bidding

SOUTH	WEST	NORTH	EAST
2 NT	Pass	3 NT	Pass
Pass	Pass		

The Lead

West leads the two of clubs to his partner's ace and East continues the suit. How do you plan the play?

Review

There are seven top tricks, and the obvious place to look for the two extra tricks you need is in the heart suit. If the heart honours are divided, you should be able to develop two more heart tricks by finessing twice against East. The snag is that dummy has only one certain entry. There is, of course, the possibility of finessing in spades against either East or West. Which card should you lead at trick three?

Solution

A first-round finesse of the ten of spades would be a dubious method of trying to gain either an entry to dummy or a trick. The better way is to run the jack of spades at trick three. If this loses to the queen, the ace and the ten of spades in dummy will serve as the entries you need to finesse twice in hearts.

The complete deal:

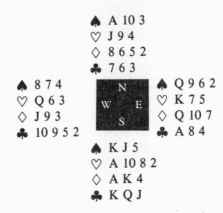

```
                 ♠ A 10 3
                 ♡ J 9 4
                 ◇ 8 6 5 2
                 ♣ 7 6 3
  ♠ 8 7 4             N        ♠ Q 9 6 2
  ♡ Q 6 3        W        E    ♡ K 7 5
  ◇ J 9 3                      ◇ Q 10 7
  ♣ 10 9 5 2          S        ♣ A 8 4
                 ♠ K J 5
                 ♡ A 10 8 2
                 ◇ A K 4
                 ♣ K Q J
```

If the jack of spades had been covered by the queen and ace, this would again have given you two entries in dummy, and you would have had a good chance of making an overtrick with three tricks in each major and two in each minor.

If the jack of spades had been allowed to win at trick three, you would have been denied a second entry to dummy. However, with three spade tricks in the bag you would need only two tricks from the hearts. You could therefore afford to play the ace and another heart, for you could lose no more than two hearts and two clubs.

PROBLEM 30

♠ 7 5
♡ J 8 4
◇ A 10 4 3
♣ A K 9 5

♠ A Q J 8 6 3
♡ 7 2
◇ Q J 6
♣ 8 3

Game all.
Dealer West.

The Bidding

WEST	NORTH	EAST	SOUTH
1 ♡	Pass	Pass	1 ♠
Pass	2 ♡	Pass	2 ♠
Pass	3 ♠	Pass	4 ♠
Pass	Pass	Pass	

The Lead

West starts with the three top hearts, East following suit as you ruff the third round. How do you plan the play?

Review

Clearly you must hope for a 3–2 trump break. There are finessing positions in both spades and diamonds, and you can afford one of these finesses to be wrong. On the bidding East can hardly have both missing kings, but it is possible for West to have them both. Is there any risk attached to finessing in both suits?

Solution

In fact if the spade finesse is working there is no need to take it, for then the diamond finesse is bound to be right as well. If the diamond finesse is wrong, the spade finesse will also be wrong and the contract will have no chance. So you must assume the diamond finesse to be right.

There is a danger in taking the spade finesse, for a further heart lead from West might enable East to uppercut with the nine or ten of spades, thereby promoting a second trump trick for the defence. It looks as though it must be right to play the ace of spades followed by the queen, removing as many of the enemy trumps as possible.

But there is a further hazard. If West has only two clubs, the defender who wins the king of spades may lock you in dummy with a club return, leaving you with no safe way back to hand to draw the last trump and finesse in diamonds. To overcome this threat you must cash dummy's top clubs before playing the second round of spades. The complete deal:

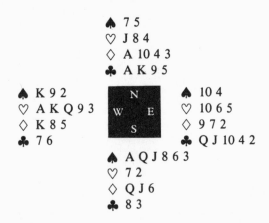

```
                    ♠ 7 5
                    ♡ J 8 4
                    ◇ A 10 4 3
                    ♣ A K 9 5
♠ K 9 2            N              ♠ 10 4
♡ A K Q 9 3    W       E          ♡ 10 6 5
◇ K 8 5            S              ◇ 9 7 2
♣ 7 6                             ♣ Q J 10 4 2
                    ♠ A Q J 8 6 3
                    ♡ 7 2
                    ◇ Q J 6
                    ♣ 8 3
```

After ruffing the third heart you cash the spade ace, play off the top clubs, and play a second spade to the queen and king. West cannot prevent you from regaining the lead, drawing the last trump and finessing in diamonds to land the game.

PROBLEM 31

♠ A Q 9 8
♡ 10 8 3
◇ 10 2
♣ 8 7 6 3

♠ J 10 4
♡ A K Q 9 7 6
◇ A Q J 6
♣ —

Game all.
Dealer South.

The Bidding

SOUTH	WEST	NORTH	EAST
2 ♡	Pass	3 ♡	Pass
4 ♣	Pass	4 ♠	Pass
6 ♡	Pass	Pass	Pass

The Lead

West leads the ace of clubs which you ruff. It takes three rounds to draw the enemy trumps, East discarding two clubs. How do you continue?

Review

There are finessing positions in both spades and diamonds, and it looks as though you should make the slam as long as at least one of the kings is favourably placed. Is it just a matter of trying the finesses one after the other, or is there something else to consider?

Solution

Naturally you must start with the spade finesse, but there is a danger that is easily overlooked. If you run the jack of spades it is likely to win, for East will hold off if he has the king. He will win the second spade and return a club for you to ruff. You will be able to enter dummy with a spade, but when you cash the last spade you will have no good discard in your hand. You will, in fact, be squeezed in diamonds. If you throw the six of diamonds, you will be able to score the three diamond tricks you need only if East has the king doubleton. Nor will it help to discard a diamond honour on the last spade, or to refuse to cash it.

You can avoid all this trouble if you make sure of testing the diamonds before running the spades. Lead the jack of spades on the first round, by all means, but cover it with the queen. If East holds up, take a finesse in diamonds before playing a second round of spades. Now you cannot be denied twelve tricks if one of the finesses is right.

The complete deal:

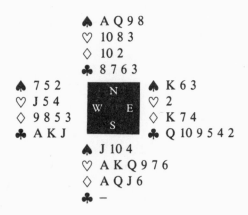

```
                ♠ A Q 9 8
                ♡ 10 8 3
                ◇ 10 2
                ♣ 8 7 6 3
  ♠ 7 5 2           N        ♠ K 6 3
  ♡ J 5 4                    ♡ 2
  ◇ 9 8 5 3     W      E     ◇ K 7 4
  ♣ A K J           S        ♣ Q 10 9 5 4 2
                ♠ J 10 4
                ♡ A K Q 9 7 6
                ◇ A Q J 6
                ♣ —
```

PROBLEM 32

♠ Q 10 7 4
♡ A J 5 2
◇ K 6
♣ J 10 6

♠ A J 9 8 6 3
♡ 7
◇ 9 8 4
♣ K Q 8

Game all.
Dealer West.

The Bidding

WEST	NORTH	EAST	SOUTH
1 ♡	Pass	Pass	1 ♠
Pass	3 ♠	Pass	4 ♠
Pass	Pass	Pass	

The Lead

West leads the king of hearts to dummy's ace. How do you plan the play?

Review

When three trumps including the king are missing the percentage play is to take the finesse. Although East cannot have much in the way of high cards there is certainly room for him to have the king of spades. Is there any valid reason for rejecting the trump finesse?

Solution

The mark of a good player in a situation like this is that he extends the chain of reasoning a little further than most. You can afford to lose a spade trick on this hand as long as you do not lose two diamond tricks as well. If East, who passed his partner's opening bid, has the king of spades, he certainly cannot have the ace of diamonds and the contract is therefore completely safe. If the spade finesse is working, in other words, there is no need to take it.

That being the case, you may as well play a spade to your ace at trick two, guarding against the possibility of West having the singleton king of spades and East the ace of diamonds.

The complete deal:

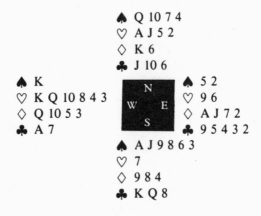

```
                    ♠ Q 10 7 4
                    ♡ A J 5 2
                    ◇ K 6
                    ♣ J 10 6
 ♠ K                                    ♠ 5 2
 ♡ K Q 10 8 4 3          N              ♡ 9 6
 ◇ Q 10 5 3         W         E         ◇ A J 7 2
 ♣ A 7                   S              ♣ 9 5 4 3 2
                    ♠ A J 9 8 6 3
                    ♡ 7
                    ◇ 9 8 4
                    ♣ K Q 8
```

PROBLEM 33

$$\spadesuit\ 6$$
$$\heartsuit\ A\ 10\ 4\ 3$$
$$\diamondsuit\ J\ 9\ 3$$
$$\clubsuit\ A\ J\ 6\ 5\ 2$$

```
      N
   W     E
      S
```

♠ Q 3
♡ 8 6

N–S game. ◇ A K Q 10 7 2
Dealer West. ♣ K 8 3

The Bidding

WEST	NORTH	EAST	SOUTH
Pass	Pass	1 ♠	2 ◇
3 ♠	5 ◇	Pass	Pass
Pass			

The Lead

West leads the king of hearts to dummy's ace. When you play the spade from the table, East goes up with the ace, cashes the jack of hearts and continues with a third heart. You ruff high as West follows with the nine. You ruff the queen of spades in dummy and draw trumps in two rounds. How should you continue?

Review

Your task is to find the queen of clubs. East might be expected to have this card in view of his opening bid, but a third-in-hand opening at favourable vulnerability does not necessarily promise much in the way of high cards. If West has the club queen a simple finesse will land the contract. Is there anything else worth trying?

Solution

There is no need for any finessing, in fact, for if West has the club queen it is bound to pop up. West is known to have the queen of hearts as well, and you have what is known as a "show-up" or "count" squeeze against him. The complete deal:

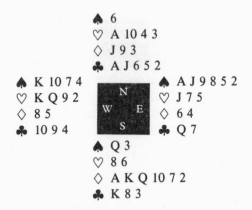

Just run the diamonds to reach this position:

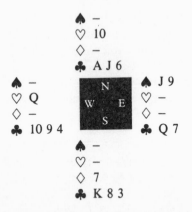

On the last diamond West discards a club and dummy the heart. When the queen of clubs does not appear from West on the second round you know the full story, so you rise with the ace and call for the queen.

PROBLEM 34

♠ A 9 5 2
♥ 8 6 3
♦ J 8 3
♣ 9 4 2

♠ Q J 10 7 6 3
♥ A Q
♦ Q 10 4
♣ A Q

Love all.
Dealer South.

The Bidding

SOUTH	WEST	NORTH	EAST
1 ♠	Pass	2 ♠	Pass
4 ♠	Pass	Pass	Pass

The Lead

West cashes the ace and king of diamonds and continues with a third diamond. To your relief East follows suit. How do you plan the play?

Review

Since you can afford to lose only one more trick, it looks as though you need to find two of the three finesses right – a fifty-fifty chance. Can you do better? Which finesses should you take and in which order?

Solution

Your chances are quite a lot better than 50% — provided that you took the precaution of unblocking in diamonds so that the lead is now in dummy. The point to bear in mind is that West, who has already produced the top diamonds and yet did not make himself heard in the bidding, is unlikely to have more than one of the missing kings. You should therefore finesse in the side suits but not in trumps.

Play a heart (or a club) from dummy and take the finesse. If it wins, cash the ace of the same suit, enter dummy with the ace of spades, ruff the third heart (or club) to eliminate the suit, and then play another trump. If West has to win, he must present you with your tenth trick in one way or another.

If your first finesse loses, win the return and play a trump to the ace. Now your only chance is that the king will drop. If it does, draw the last trump and finesse in the other suit to land your game.

The complete deal:

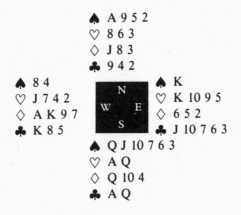

<table>
<tr><td></td><td>♠ A 9 5 2</td><td></td></tr>
<tr><td></td><td>♡ 8 6 3</td><td></td></tr>
<tr><td></td><td>◇ J 8 3</td><td></td></tr>
<tr><td></td><td>♣ 9 4 2</td><td></td></tr>
</table>

♠ 8 4		♠ K
♡ J 7 4 2	N	♡ K 10 9 5
◇ A K 9 7	W E	◇ 6 5 2
♣ K 8 5	S	♣ J 10 7 6 3

        ♠ Q J 10 7 6 3
        ♡ A Q
        ◇ Q 10 4
        ♣ A Q

PROBLEM 35

```
                    ♠ Q J 4
                    ♡ J 8 5 4
                    ◇ A K 10
                    ♣ Q 5 3

                    ┌─────────┐
                    │    N    │
                    │  W   E  │
                    │    S    │
                    └─────────┘

                    ♠ 7
                    ♡ A K Q
Love all.           ◇ Q 7 5
Dealer North.       ♣ A J 10 7 6 2
```

The Bidding

WEST	NORTH	EAST	SOUTH
	1 NT	Pass	2 ♣
2 ♠	Pass	Pass	3 ♣
Pass	3 ◇	Pass	3 ♡
Pass	3 NT	Pass	4 ♣
Pass	4 ◇	Pass	6 ♣
Pass	Pass	Pass	

The Lead

West cashes the ace of spades and switches to the nine of hearts. How do you plan the play?

Review

You need to avoid a trump loser and, with four cards missing, the finesse is clearly the right play. So you are going to cross to dummy in diamonds in order to take the trump finesse. Furthermore, it must be right to play the queen of clubs from the table in order to retain the lead for a further finesse. Is there anything else to think about?

Solution

There is always the possibility of a 4–0 club break. If East has K 9 8 4 in clubs he will cover the queen on the first round, and you will need two further entries in dummy to pick up his trumps. You might try to gain an extra entry by finessing the ten of diamonds on the second round, but if West is awake he will spike your guns by putting in the jack. That will leave you short of an entry and you will have to concede a trump trick.

A little forethought avoids all this trouble. At trick three you should prepare for the possibility of a later entry-finesse in diamonds by leading the queen of diamonds to dummy's king. Now, when East covers the queen of clubs and West shows out, the way is clear for a finesse against the jack of diamonds.

The complete deal:

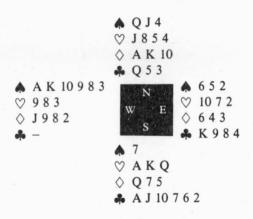

```
                    ♠ Q J 4
                    ♡ J 8 5 4
                    ◇ A K 10
                    ♣ Q 5 3
♠ A K 10 9 8 3                      ♠ 6 5 2
♡ 9 8 3             N              ♡ 10 7 2
◇ J 9 8 2        W     E           ◇ 6 4 3
♣ —                 S              ♣ K 9 8 4
                    ♠ 7
                    ♡ A K Q
                    ◇ Q 7 5
                    ♣ A J 10 7 6 2
```

If the clubs behave more reasonably, of course, you will never need to finesse against the jack of diamonds. Your third diamond will eventually be discarded on the jack of hearts.

PROBLEM 36

♠ Q 9 5 2
♡ A Q 3
◇ J 10 9 7 2
♣ 5

```
      N
   W     E
      S
```

♠ A J 6 3
♡ 6
◇ K Q 8 4
♣ A J 8 3

N–S game.
Dealer South.

The Bidding

SOUTH	WEST	NORTH	EAST
1 ◇	2 ♣	3 ◇	Dble*
Rdble	4 ♡	5 ◇	Pass
Pass	Dble	Pass	Pass
Pass			

* Competitive double, showing length in both majors.

The Lead

West starts with the ace and another diamond, East discarding a spade on the second round. How should you play?

Review

East's shape is likely to be 5–5–1–2, although it is just possible that it is 5–4–1–3. A count of your tricks reveals four trumps in dummy, the ace of clubs, the ace of hearts and two heart ruffs in hand, plus two spades for a total of ten. It looks as though an eleventh trick can come only from a strip-squeeze and spade end-play against East.

The snag is that when you play dummy's last trump East will come down to three spades and a winning heart, and he will be able to take two tricks when you let him in. Can you see any way round the problem?

Solution

The end-play will work only if you keep the ace of hearts in dummy to control the position. That means taking a hazardous finesse of the queen of hearts, hoping for the full hand to be:

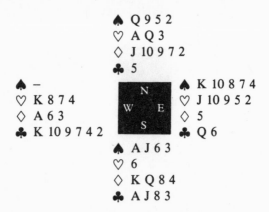

Draw a third round of trumps and lead a heart for a finesse of the queen. Ruff the small heart, cash the club ace and ruff a club. After a spade to the ace (you can afford the extravagance), East feels the pinch when you ruff a club in this position:

If East discards a spade you can easily establish two extra tricks in the suit. If he discards a heart, you cash the heart ace to extract his last heart and then play the queen of spades to end-play him.